Survival

Chris Buckton

Illustrated by
Paul Savage

 FULL FLIGHT

Titles in Full Flight 3

Badger Publishing Limited
26 Wedgwood Way, Pin Green Industrial Estate, Stevenage,
Hertfordshire SG1 4QF
Telephone: 01438 356907. Fax: 01438 747015.
www.badger-publishing.co.uk
enquiries@badger-publishing.co.uk

Survival   ISBN 1 84424 243 9

Text © Chris Buckton 2004
Series editing © Jonny Zucker 2004
Complete work © Badger Publishing Limited 2004

Series Editor: Jonny Zucker
Publisher: David Jamieson
Editor: Paul Martin
Design: Jain Birchenough
Cover illustration: Paul Savage
Printed and bound in China through Colorcraft Ltd., Hong Kong

Survival

Chris Buckton

Illustrated by Paul Savage

Contents

Badger Publishing

Chapter 1 - "We Can Trust Them"

"Whatever you do, remember to stay together."

It was the first time Mark and Pete had gone climbing on their own. They were camping with their parents. They'd spotted a mountain that looked quite easy to climb. They begged to have a go.

"You know we're good climbers," said Mark. "We know all the safety rules."

"And we'll stay on the track," promised Pete. "It's a fine day."

"The weather forecast said there would be mist later in the afternoon," warned Dad.

"We'll be back by then," promised Pete.

Their parents looked at each other.

Mum nodded. "I think we can trust them," she said. "We can drive into town while they're climbing."

"Have you thought about what to take with you?" asked Dad.

"We've made a list," said Mark.

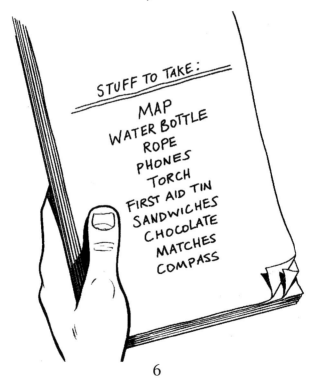

STUFF TO TAKE:
MAP
WATER BOTTLE
ROPE
PHONES
TORCH
FIRST AID TIN
SANDWICHES
CHOCOLATE
MATCHES
COMPASS

"Well done," said Dad. "I'm glad to see you thinking for yourselves. Who's going to get everything together?"

"We are!"

The boys worked fast. They were keen to be climbing. They checked their climbing boots, tying the laces tightly and turning down the thick socks.

At last they were ready. They each carried a backpack.

Dad said it again: "Whatever you do -"

"We know, stay together!" laughed the boys.

Chapter 2 - Higher and Higher

The going was quite easy at first. It was good weather for climbing, not too hot, and the breeze gave them energy.

"I could climb forever on a day like this!" shouted Mark.

"I could make it up Everest!" boasted Pete. They followed the grass track along the side of the mountain. The path was rocky further ahead. They could see a waterfall sparkling in the sun.

"Let's get to the rocks and then stop for lunch," panted Mark. It was getting steeper now.

They found a flat rock to sit on while
they ate their lunch. They looked down
into the valley far below.

"Look, you can see the camp site."

"The cars look as if you could pick them
up!"

9

"And there's the road going to town."

There was nobody else in sight on the mountain. The only sound was the rushing water as it fell over the rocks.

"This is the life!" said Pete, as he lay back in the sun. "Just wait till we tell the guys back at school."

"We're not at the top yet," warned Mark.

"We soon will be." Pete jumped up. "Come on, let's get going!"

Chapter 3 - "Stay on the Track!"

The boys climbed slowly now. They had to scramble over rocks. They couldn't see the top of the mountain.

"Our water bottle's empty," said Mark as he took the last swig. "Let's fill it from the waterfall. The water's really clean up here."

The waterfall was a little way off the track but they would be able to get back easily.

"Stay on the track!" joked Mark in his dad's voice. They laughed as they left the track and clambered across to the waterfall. Pete went first. Mark followed, holding the water bottle.

Suddenly they heard a low moaning.
It sounded like a trapped animal.

"What was that?" asked Mark.

"Don't know," said Pete, moving
towards the sound.

Pete suddenly stopped. He'd found something on the ground. It gleamed white in the sun.

"It's a ram's skull!" he shouted.

"Well that noise didn't come from a ram's skull," called Mark. "It came from a real, live animal."

"There are no real, live animals anywhere up here," Pete replied, picking up the skull.

They were quite a long way from the track now. The waterfall was very steep.

"It's getting too dangerous," shouted Mark. "Let's forget about the water and get back to the track."

Mark looked down. He felt a chill of fear and suddenly lost his footing. The water bottle fell out of his hands and bounced from rock to rock. It disappeared into the valley below.

"You idiot!" shouted Pete.

"I didn't do it on purpose," Mark replied, getting his balance back. They slowly made their way back to the track. Pete was holding the ram's skull.

"Get rid of that thing," said Mark. "It gives me the creeps."

Pete found a triangle of rocks and put the skull on top of them. At that moment two climbers came round the corner of the track. They were coming down the mountain. One of them called out.

"Hello there. Are you coming or going?"

"We're on our way up," answered Pete.

"It's probably best to turn back," said the climber. "There's mist at the top And it can get thick very quickly."

Chapter 4 - Turning Back

Mark watched the climbers until they were out of sight. Suddenly he felt scared.

"Pete!" he said. "You heard what they said. We should start back."

But Pete wouldn't listen. "It's not far. We can't give up now."

He started climbing again. "Pete, come back!" shouted Mark.

"You're a wimp!" laughed Pete.

"I'm not coming with you," shouted Mark.

"Think I care?"

"We promised to stay together!"

"Well, you'll just have to come too. I'm not turning back now."

"How can you be so stupid? We could get lost in the mist!"

Pete went on climbing. "Scaredy cat!"

Mark looked up towards the mountain top. He could see mist swirling round the highest peak. "I'm going back down. And so will you if you have any sense."

Pete stopped and looked back at Mark. He shrugged. "See you later then," he shouted at Mark. Mark turned his back on his brother and started down the track.

Chapter 5 - "Think I Care?"

Mark walked slowly. He was sure that Pete would soon follow him. Every now and then he stopped and turned round, hoping to see his brother coming down the track. He could still see the skull on the rocks where Pete had left it. It seemed to bc smiling at him.

He gave one last yell. "Pete!" His voice echoed round the rocks. No answer.

"Think I care?" he shouted. Why should he worry? He'd done the right thing.

Maybe Pete was teasing him. "I bet he's tracking me," he thought.

"And then he'll jump out at me." He stopped and listened. He could hear the waterfall. Nothing else.

It was quite hard climbing down. The rocks were slippery. Sometimes Mark couldn't see the track clearly and he had to stop. It would be really difficult in the mist. What if Pete missed the track and fell into the waterfall? But he still felt angry with his brother.

"It's not my fault," he told himself. "I tried to make him see sense. I hope he gets a real scare. It would serve him right."

There was a notice by the edge of the waterfall. He hadn't seen it on the way up.

His heart was beating. Maybe he
should go after Pete and warn him.

Then he remembered his mobile.
Brilliant! He could phone Pete. But
there was no reply when he tried.

Chapter 6 - On His Own

Meanwhile, Pete was climbing higher. He kept his eyes fixed on the top of the mountain. It was covered in mist but not too far away. He knew he could make it. All he thought about was the pride of reaching the top.

As he got nearer, the mist surrounded him. It was much colder now, and the mist felt wet on his face. Drops hung on his cap and got into his eyes. It was so quiet inside the mist that every sound was muffled. He couldn't even hear the waterfall.

But standing on the top made it all worthwhile.

He ate some chocolate, feeling like the king of the world. A shaft of sunlight broke through the mist for a moment. He could see right down into the valley below. He thought about Mark. He must be back at the camp site by now. What a fool to miss this view.

Then the mist folded back like a great blanket, and Pete was shut inside. He couldn't see anything.

He knew he had to get down but he wasn't sure which side he'd come up.

He realised with dismay that Mark had got the map. But maybe his compass could help. He got it out of the backpack and found north. He had to think really hard to work out the direction of the camp site. He thought he remembered seeing the sun set in the west behind this mountain. So he needed to go east.

And there was the track! He was right. Pete felt quite proud of himself. He'd be back in no time now. Mark wouldn't have much to say when he told his story back at school!

Chapter 7 - "Don't Ask Me"

By the time Mark reached the camp site he was sure that Pete was tracking him. Trying to give him a scare. Well, it wouldn't work. He would pretend not to notice. So he stopped looking back at the mountain and carried on as if nothing had happened.

His parents weren't back from their shopping trip. He took his boots off and lay down on his sleeping bag. He felt bad that he'd turned back. Maybe Pete was right, he was a wimp.

He was woken by his dad's voice. "Had a good climb?"

"Yeah, great." Mark looked away and yawned.

"Where's Pete?"

Mark shrugged. "Dunno. Don't ask me. Somewhere around."

Chapter 8 - Lost in the Mist

Pete was starting to worry. It was very hard to see the track in the mist, and he kept straying off it.

He couldn't tell how far he'd come. But surely he must be near the place they had stopped for lunch. He seemed to be walking forever.

He came to a fork in the track. He didn't remember noticing it on the way up. He had no idea which way to go. If he chose the wrong track he might end up in the waterfall. Maybe he'd been on the wrong track all along.

He began to shiver. He was utterly lost.

And without a water bottle.

He rubbed his hands together to warm them. His socks felt wet. He knew wet clothes were dangerous. He stamped his feet and wriggled his toes. They felt numb. He would need shelter if he had to stay here all night. Maybe he could find a corner between two rocks. That's what sheep did.

What a fool he'd been. I'll probably die out here he thought and Mark will think it's his fault.

Then a sound made Pete jump. A moaning, coming from nearby. Like a trapped animal, Pete thought. And then he remembered... the ram's skull!

Chapter 9 - "It's All My Fault"

When Pete didn't turn up for supper, Mark knew he'd got to tell the truth. The words choked him and he felt really bad. But Dad didn't yell at him or blame him. He rang the ranger and reported Pete as missing.

Waiting was the worst part. Nobody felt like eating supper. I shouldn't have let him go on alone thought Mark. He imagined Pete's body bouncing from rock to rock like the water bottle.

His mum put an arm round him. "It will be OK," she told him. But he didn't believe her. He knew she was scared too.

It was almost dark when a police car drove into the camp site. The mist was not only on the mountain, it surrounded the camp site too.

A policeman and two rangers climbed out. Pete wasn't with them. "I'm really sorry," said the policeman, "it's almost impossible to see through the mist. We'll have to look again in the morning."

By now everyone was frantic about Pete. He might not make it through a night up there. It was so wet and cold.

At that moment, a figure walked out of the mist. It was Pete! Mark and his parents ran over to him.

"Thank God you're OK," Mum sighed.

"We thought you were dead," said Mark.

"I would have been," Pete replied. "If it hadn't been for this." He held up the ram's skull.

"What do you mean?" asked Dad. But Pete had already wandered off with Mark.

"Well," said the policeman, "let's hope they've learned just how dangerous mountains can be. Now I suggest you all get some sleep."

***

"I know it sounds weird," Pete told his brother, "but when I was really lost, I heard that moaning sound and walked towards it. It led me back to the ram's skull."

Mark nodded and looked at the skull. "Told you it was creepy," he whispered. "It's not coming in the tent with us is it?"

Pete shook his head and put the skull on the ground. "It made a moaning sound the whole way down the mountain, when I was on the right track. If I went wrong it stayed silent. That's the how I made it."

Mark smiled. "I'm glad you made it back OK," he said to his brother.

"Me too," said Pete. "Next time we go climbing, I reckon we should stay together."

They climbed into their tent and zipped up the door.

A few feet away the ram's skull gave off a white glow and what sounded like laughter echoed from its mouth.